Maverick
Early Readers

'Surfer Chimp'
An original concept by Alison Donald
© Alison Donald

Illustrated by Gareth Robinson

Published by MAVERICK ARTS PUBLISHING LTD
Studio 11, City Business Centre, 6 Brighton Road,
Horsham, West Sussex, RH13 5BB
© Maverick Arts Publishing Limited November 2019
+44 (0)1403 256941

A CIP catalogue record for this book is available at the British Library.

ISBN 978-1-84886-632-4

Maverick
publishing
www.maverickbooks.co.uk

Yellow

This book is rated as: Yellow Band (Guided Reading)
This story is decodable at Letters and Sounds Phase 3/4.

Surfer Chimp

by **Alison Donald**

illustrated by
Gareth Robinson

Chaz spotted a contest at the beach.

Chaz was all set to surf.

The surfers all set off.

Chaz did not zoom along.

He spotted a fish.

Chaz got on top of a wave.

11

Chaz floated along.

He spotted a crab.

Chaz did a flip in the air.

Chaz spotted an octopus.

Eeee, ee, eee!

Chaz did a big jump.

Chaz spotted a fin.

Chaz was the winner!

But Chaz ran on and on.

Quiz

1. What does Chaz join?
a) A talent show
b) A running race
c) A surfing contest

2. What did Chaz spot first?
a) A fish
b) A jellyfish
c) A bird

3. Chaz did a _____ in the air.
a) Dive
b) Flip
c) Flop

4. What scared Chaz?

a) A baboon

b) A shark

c) A cat

5. What place did Chaz win?

a) First

b) Second

c) Third

Turn over for answers

Book Bands for Guided Reading

The Institute of Education book banding system is a scale of colours that reflects the various levels of reading difficulty. The bands are assigned by taking into account the content, the language style, the layout and phonics. Word, phrase and sentence level work is also taken into consideration.

Maverick Early Readers are a bright, attractive range of books covering the pink to white bands. All of these books have been book banded for guided reading to the industry standard and edited by a leading educational consultant.

To view the whole Maverick Readers scheme, visit our website at

www.maverickearlyreaders.com

Or scan the QR code above to view our scheme instantly!

Pink

Red

Yellow

Blue

Green

Orange

Turquoise

Purple

Gold

White

Quiz Answers: 1c, 2a, 3b, 4b, 5a